King in a Stable

Also by Jenny Robertson
The Encyclopedia of Bible Stories
Fior
Circle of Shadows

First published 1977 by Scripture Union
47 Marylebone Lane, London W1M 6AX

ISBN 0-87239-123x

2990 ⟨s|u⟩® $4.95

Designed by Tony Cantale

Printed in Great Britain by
Purnell & Sons Ltd., Paulton, Bristol

King
in a Stable

Text by Jenny Robertson
Illustrations by Sheila Bewley

STANDARD PUBLISHING

Cincinnati, Ohio   2990

Night brought the townsfolk home, hurrying to safety behind the walls of Bethlehem. Bethlehem was very old, hundreds of years old. It was sometimes called David's town, because it had been the home of the shepherd boy who became king over his people. Ancient white-walled Bethlehem was a special town: the town of God's promise. 'Little Bethlehem,' read the promise, 'the smallest town of all, I am giving you a King, a Child born before the worlds began. The young mother will bring her firstborn son to birth. He will guide my people and care for their hurts. His kingdom shall spread to the ends of the earth.' Bethlehem lay within its white walls awaiting the birth of its King.

Not far
from Bethlehem, an
orange moon rose eerily
above the streets of
Jerusalem, the capital
city. It was too
stuffy to sleep and the
poor people, who had no
watered gardens, thronged
the narrow streets. Their king,
Herod, strolled in his cool courtyard.

   Herod knew everyone hated him,
even though he had built a
magnificent temple where people
begged God for the promised King to
come and set them free.

Herod knew his people listened carefully when the priests unrolled their huge, heavy scrolls and read out the words and promises of their God. King Herod was a foreigner, coming from a country in the south. He did not pay attention to the words on the scrolls, but he wanted to win the people's favor and that is why he had hired thousands of workmen to build the beautiful temple.

Pilgrims came to pray there from all over the world. In the courtyard coins rattled above the drumming of hoofs as calves and lambs were led off to be killed. People offered the animals to God as a way of asking Him to wipe out all the wrong things they knew they had done. The lowing and bleating mingled with the singing of people whose hearts overflowed with such joy and longing that tears streamed down their upturned faces. They longed for the day when God's promised King would reign in splendor, making the land glad and bringing the people peace. They loved and worshipped the God they had never seen.

Priests in long-fringed shawls cast lots. An old priest called Zechariah was chosen to go into the very heart of the temple, the Holy of Holies. There, before the seven-branched candlestick on the altar, he burned sweet-smelling incense while the people outside prayed. Zechariah loved God and went gladly into the dark shrine where only priests might go.

It was very quiet in the holy place, far from the noise and clamor of the temple courtyard. Zechariah watched the incense burn; then he fell on his knees. In the glowing darkness he saw the shape of a man—a messenger from God.

'Don't be afraid, Zechariah! God has heard your prayers. Your wife, Elizabeth, will have a baby. You must call him John. The promised King is coming. Your little boy will be his herald, running on ahead, announcing the news to everyone.'

Zechariah looked up, startled. 'I am an old man, and my wife is old. Have you no sign to show me that this will be so?'

'I have come from God with this message, Zechariah. Because you have not believed you will be unable to speak until my promise to you comes true.'

Zechariah lifted his hand and tried to speak but no words came. The figure faded, leaving Zechariah alone in the candlelit room, while the incense burned on the altar and the smoke drifted upward.

Zechariah did not speak until the baby was born. 'How wonderful! Zechariah and Elizabeth are old enough to be grandparents, and now they have their own baby,' admired all the relations.

'He'll be called Zechariah, of course,' they all agreed.

'No!' Elizabeth said firmly. 'We are going to call him John.'

'You can't! No one in our family is called that!' Zechariah made signs for a writing tablet to be brought to him. In the soft wax he wrote in big, clear letters: 'His name is John.'

At that moment Zechariah found his voice. He covered his head with his prayer shawl. In his innermost mind thoughts from God took shape. He opened his mouth and praised God. 'God is so good to us! He has come to His people as He promised. He is sending a wonderful Savior, one who belongs to David's family.'

Zechariah took his baby son into his arms. 'You, my little child, you shall be called a herald of the Most High. You are to make His road ready for Him, and tell His people that their sins will be forgiven. He is coming like the dawn after a long night. The Child promised before the worlds began is coming to bring light to those who dwell in darkness, in the shadow of death. He will take our hands and lead us gently along the pathway of peace.'

Far away in the north, in Galilee, was the quiet town of Nazareth. One of Elizabeth's relatives lived there, a young girl called Mary. 'Nothing good comes out of Nazareth!' people in Jerusalem often joked.

But Mary didn't mind. Joseph lived in Nazareth too. Joseph was the woodworker and builder. He had grown up in Nazareth but his home town was Bethlehem. Joseph belonged to the family of King David.

His strong hard hands clasped Mary's firmly. Mary's lovely dark eyes were solemn as Joseph promised to marry her.

'I shall be a bride,' Mary thought, 'and wear a headdress of silver coins. Then I'll become Joseph's wife. If God is good to us I shall have a child, Joseph's baby, to nurse and love and care for.' Her eyes grew big and full of dreams.

Mary was daydreaming about Joseph and their wedding as she turned a heavy stone, grinding barley grain into flour to bake the family's bread.

'Mary, Mary! The Lord is with you. He is making you wonderfully glad!'

It was a voice more beautiful than anything she had ever heard, yet she was worried.

'Mary, don't be afraid! You will have a baby. His name is Jesus.'

'That means "Savior,"' thought Mary.
'Has God chosen me to be the mother of
the promised King: the King all my people
long for?'
'I have no husband yet,' she said aloud.
'God's Holy Spirit will rest
upon you. Your child will be holy, God's
own Son.'
'Let it be as you have said.' She bowed
her head, giving her consent.
Then she was left alone with the heavy
stones, and the grain piled in its basket. God's
messenger had gone, yet God's word remained.
It changed her life, and the life of
all the world. 'What will Joseph
say?' she wondered anxiously. 'Will he
want to marry me? Whatever
will my family think? And
everyone else? The whole of
Nazareth will talk about me.
Cousin Elizabeth! I will visit her.
She will understand.'

Joseph did not understand.

'How can I marry Mary now?' The question beat in his brain like a hammer, troubling his sleep. He got up each morning more wearily than he had lain down.

He could not even speak to Mary. She had gone all the way to a city of Judah to stay with Elizabeth.

'I cannot marry Mary,' Joseph decided in the end.

That night as he lay on his sleeping mat, God's messenger came to him and spoke to him in his dreams.

'Joseph, descendant of King David, don't be afraid to marry Mary. God's Holy Spirit has begun the life of the baby within her. She will have a son and you must call Him Jesus, because He has come to save His people from their sins.'

Joseph sighed in his sleep. He sensed a bright hand held over him. His hurt, troubled mind was eased. That night his sleep was deep. He leapt up in the morning.

'I am going to marry Mary!' he announced to his family.

Mary married Joseph when she came back from Elizabeth's house. The people of Nazareth went on talking for some time.

'So Mary and Joseph got married, after all,' said Hannah, stopping to chat with her sister one day, while little Benjamin played.

'She seems happy. She must know that everyone is talking, but she holds her head high. I saw her on my way from the well. Still, I mustn't stop. Come along, Benjamin. Why, there's your father!' Hannah said good-bye to her sister and went across to her husband. He had important news.

'Caesar in Rome has ordered a census of all people. Our rulers want an exact record of us all. Everyone has to go to his own hometown to be counted. What an upheaval it will mean!' He put Benjamin on the donkey and they set off for home.

Mary heard Joseph hammering as she came home from the well. The sign outside their house read: 'Woodworker. The yokes I carve for oxen are easy to bear. Boats, plows and furniture I make and repair.' As she came in, Mary saw that although Joseph's broad fingers were busy, his mind was not on his work.

'Mary, we must make a long journey.'

She set down her heavy jar. 'Is it the census? We have to go and be counted?'

'Yes, I must go to Bethlehem, since I am a descendant of David. But how can you travel? The baby will soon be born.'

'Our baby will be born in Bethlehem, Joseph, if the time comes while we are there.'

'Of course!'

'Joseph, the Roman rulers make us travel to be counted, yet I feel God wants us to go.'

Mary packed their
things. Then they set off
on their long journey. Each
night they slept rolled in
blankets on the bare ground beside
the fire that Joseph lit to warm them
and keep wolves and jackals away.
'Mary must be so uncomfortable,' thought
Joseph. To his surprise he saw that she was
smiling as the patient donkey jolted her over the
rough road.
'We have such a long way to go,' Joseph sighed.
'God will look after us!' Mary's tired face shone with joy.

When they reached Bethlehem, crowds jostled and pressed against them. Everywhere was full. Giggling children shared their sleeping mats. Mary and Joseph found the inn.

'There's no room!' The innkeeper turned away.

'Please!' Joseph begged. 'Haven't you anything at all?'

'There are stables back of the inn. Over there! I'm rushed off my feet but I'll light the way. It's the best we can do. Never been so busy before!'

'You must be very tired,' Mary sympathized.

'I am! You're the first person to notice, though. Look, I'll leave you my lamp.'

In the stable among the animals the promised Child was born. Tenderly Mary held Him to her. She wrapped Him tightly in strips of linen. She laid the baby in a manger on fresh rustling hay. Joseph fell asleep, but Mary lay gazing in drowsy wonder at her sleeping child.

Outside the
town shepherds
huddled around
the fire.
'Bethlehem was busy
today,' they agreed.
'I suppose all the folk are
bedded down now. Just like
our sheep!' Beyond the sheepfold soared
the white moon. Sheep stirred and
bleated. Out on the hills a wolf howled.
A cold wind ruffled the fleece of their
pet sheep and snatched at the drifting smoke.
'Play to us, Mishael.'
Young Mishael's long fingers coaxed lilting
melodies from his flute. The wind, sighing
through the olive trees, tossed the music away
into the night, while within the white-walled town a
newborn baby slumbered in a stable.
Suddenly, brighter than the flickering flames, light
fell on their faces. They heard music. Mishael laid aside
his flute. 'It sounds as golden as the light; yet I am afraid.'
'The glory of the Lord lights the sky like the summer
sun!' the shepherds cried, staring upward.

The light came closer and now it had a shape, the shape of a man, robed in majesty and splendor. He wore no jewels, nor golden crown, yet a great glory shone through him and in him and all around him. 'Don't be afraid.' The sound of his voice was more splendid than the singing in the temple, yet the words were so ordinary that the shepherds began to feel happy. 'I am God's messenger.'

He held out his hand to them. His face was grave, yet mirrored mirth. All the laughter the shepherds had known shone in his eyes. 'I bring you great news that will make everyone glad. Your Savior was born tonight in Bethlehem. You will find the promised Child wrapped in strips of linen, lying on hay in a feeding-trough.' Suddenly vast companies of God's messengers circled singing around the shepherds, who could hardly bear the beauty, yet would not look away and lose it for a moment. The shepherds' far-seeing eyes shone. The songs that gave glory to God filled their hearts. They looked like princes, but did not know it, for they had forgotten themselves in the wonder of the worship of God.

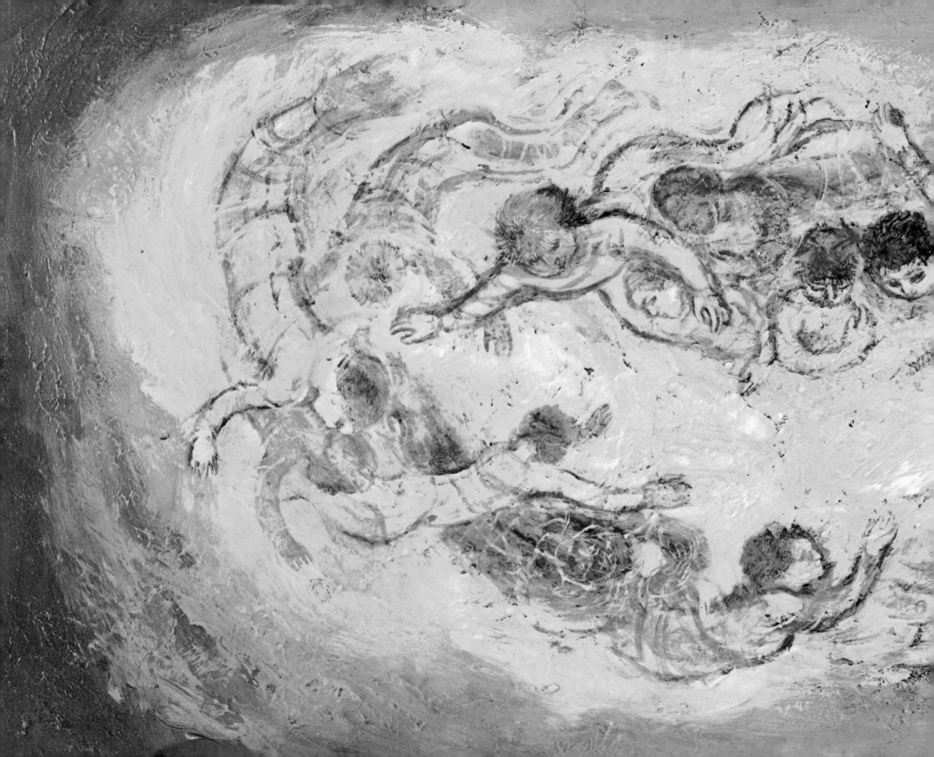

The angels disappeared
and the light faded.
   'How they sang,' said
Mishael dreamily. 'Glory
to God, peace on earth. . . .'
   'To those who please God,' added a
shepherd. 'Let's go to Bethlehem at once, as
the Lord told us.'
   'Who will guard the sheep?'
   'God will look after them. Come on.'

When the shepherds found the stable, they went in slowly, full of wonder.

'Is the newborn Child here? God's messenger told us the Savior is born.'

Joseph moved the lamp. The dim light fell on the child Mary held. Deep in thought, Joseph went to tend the donkey.

The shepherds, still dazzled by the splendor
they had seen, crowded round.
'Wrapped in linen, as the messenger said.
Does He sleep in a feeding-trough?' one
of them asked.
Mary nodded. 'The hay is hollowed
where He lay. I lifted Him when I
heard your footsteps.'
'Everything is exactly as the
messenger told us.'
'The music of highest Heaven
played for Him,' Mishael said
softly. 'Yet He lies here in a stable.'
'What kind of King is this?' they
wondered.

Muffled against the biting wind that blew endlessly in their faces, the Wise-men wondered about the King, too. They journeyed across the desert, in the tracks of long trade routes, travelling at night, for they followed a star.

'We watched it rise,' they reminded each other as they lay to rest beside their kneeling camels, 'and so we left our lovely cities and libraries of learning. Yet we sleep more peacefully here on the hard ground than we did on soft couches in shuttered rooms. Each night when we wake and see the star we forget our weariness and hurry on.'

'It's the birth-sign of the Savior all the world longs for.'

'The star leads toward Jerusalem. Let us ask King Herod where the Child is.'

'But the new King will be greater than Herod. He deserves the gifts we have chosen from our treasury of Eastern riches.'

The Wise-men came to
Herod, but he knew
nothing about the birth
of a King.
'Can the star be wrong?'
The Wise-men were uneasy.
Herod was upset, too,
and so were his rulers in
Jerusalem.
'Many people talk
about the coming of a King.
Nonsense! *I* am the King,'
stormed Herod. 'Fetch the
priests!'
When they arrived he asked,
'Where is the promised child to
be born?'
'In Bethlehem.' The priests
bowed, but they despised their foreign
king who did not know God's promises.
'So runs the saying: "Little Bethlehem, I am
giving you a King who will guide my people."'
'Go to Bethlehem,' Herod told the Wise-
men. 'Find out everything you can about . . .'
he paused, unable to say 'King,' '. . . about
the Child. Then let me know, for I should like
to honor Him with presents also.'
The Wise-men bowed and went their way.
The smell of spices lingered on in Herod's room.

The Wise-men were glad when they left
Herod's palace.
'We made a mistake,' one of them said,
'when we thought the Child would be born
in the courts of that cruel king.'
'But look! There is the star. It's
leading us on!'
They came to Bethlehem and coaxed
their camels through the narrow streets.
The star stopped above a small, plain house.
Joseph stared in surprise as the travellers,
their dusty robes smelling strangely of
spices, came to the door.
Kneeling, they offered their treasures:
dark gold, frankincense and sweet-smelling
myrrh. Mary, alarmed, drew back: 'Kings
wear gold, priests burn incense to God, but
mourning women anoint their dead with
myrrh. My child is God's Son, our King,
born to save His people. Why do they bring
myrrh as though for a burial?' she
pondered.
In a dream God warned the Wise-men that
Herod planned to kill the Child. They
journeyed home a different way.

Mary's Child grew with a beauty in His life that made her think again and again about God's promises. Others noticed Jesus too.

'There's something wonderful about Jesus,' chattered the women at the well. 'He is always busy, but He has time for everyone. See how He still carries water for Mary.'

Mary overheard. If God had chosen rich parents for His Son, Jesus would have been brought up with learning and every comfort. Instead, He willingly did all the hard work at home.

'My son,' Mary grieved, 'are You to be so lowly a King? Will people believe? Will they be drawn by the great love and caring in Your eyes, and know You are their promised King?'

Jesus walked barefoot over the hot, hard earth, and the words He learned from the holy scrolls sang in His heart, molding His mind, teaching Him about God and the promises. Slowly He grew in wisdom and stature, in favor with God and man. Some day the King who had come to the stable would become the Savior of His people.